D0480948

B
Q

JOANNA TROLLOPE

Faith

A
BLOOMSBURY
QUID

First published in Great Britain 1996

Copyright © 1996 by Joanna Trollope

The moral right of the author has been asserted

Bloomsbury Publishing Plc,
2 Soho Square, London W1V 6HB

A CIP catalogue record for this book
is available from the British Library

ISBN 0 7475 2898 5

Typeset by Hewer Text Composition Services,
Edinburgh
Printed by St Edmundsbury Press, Suffolk
Jacket design by Jeff Fisher

When my mother died, she left me a bookstore. In England, you would call it a bookshop, but I prefer the word store. It suggests a treasure house to me, a place full of riches and surprises. 'Shop' is more pedestrian. A shop is for the purchase of kettles and bacon and birdseed.

My mother's bookstore is in a town some two hours' drive east of Seattle and a hundred miles south of the Canadian border. It was settled by Scandinavians in the last century and if it has a domestic symbol, it must be the coffee pot. The whole town is crazy about coffee, addicted to it. There is a coffee shop, one of a national chain, opposite my mother's bookstore, and all day long people run in and out of it for pints and quarts of coffee in giant Styrofoam cups, carrying them back to their automobiles and places of work with a kind of tender greed.

Because we are so close to the Canadian border, and so far west, Alaskans come down to our town in the winter in search of warmth and work. A lot of them end up sleeping rough or in the beaten-up taxis they ply without a proper licence. Sometimes I find them sleeping in the bookstore doorway, and I give them money to go and buy coffee in the shop across the street. I'm sorry for them, but I don't want them in my doorway. The other immigrants are Asians from the Pacific Rim, mostly Vietnamese, who inhabit a dangerous and feuding underworld. They slip through our town on their way between Seattle and Spokane, eluding gang vendetta. Neither they, nor the drug-mazed Alaskans, have any use in the world for a bookstore specialising in English literature.

Although she never said so directly, I believe my mother opened her bookstore to console herself for disappointment in marriage. She was English and not of a generation to abandon a bad marriage and in any case, my grandmother had been a Catholic and a pious woman and had instilled into my mother that vows were vows. My grandmother died when my mother was twenty, and left her daughter in the care of her father, a good-natured, romantic man who managed a small theatre in Yorkshire, a pretty little theatre built in the time of the English Regency. My grandfather had no religion, my mother said, but he had dreams. Once, I knew, his dreams had got him into serious trouble, but of that my mother would say nothing.

Sometimes I wonder if I have taken after him. I am not a religious woman in any way but I have noticed that I have sometimes given way to dreams. My most intense dream was when I was twenty-four, and contemplating going to Boston to work in a distinguished publishing house, and I fell in love with a man in our town. He was married, with three children, and I had known him all my life, and I fell in love with a violence that quite terrified me. We had an affair, all one summer; I shall never forget it. And then quite suddenly he told me it was impossible, it was over, he was leaving. He collected up his wife and his children and, in the exaggerated way of people in this vast country of ours, took off across seven states to Greensboro, North Carolina, where he vanished, like a stone thrown into a pool. I still cannot look at the daily weather charts on television with any equanimity when the weather girl's hand sweeps over the southeastern states.

My mother took me back in, after the death of that dream. She made me a bedroom in the apartment above the store, and she gave me customers to look after and shelves to dust and arrange. My father, by then, was living in a two-room condo on the edge of Elliott Bay, in Seattle. My mother had bought the condo, and settled him there, along with his typewriter and his wardrobe of lumberjack shirts and his eloquent, empty declarations of one day being a renowned novelist, a chronicler of his time and the American Northwest. It was those declarations that had once made my mother fall in love with him. And I believe that it was those same declarations, after twenty years of talk and drink and quarter-finished manuscripts, that finally set her teeth on edge.

My mother determined to make a bookstore unlike any bookstore she had known in her English childhood. They were stiff, hushed places, she said, where one whispered as if in church, and was not allowed to touch books without specific intention of purchase. My mother's bookstore was in a converted dance studio – Latin American tangos were once taught there to combat the effect of our low grey winter skies – and she divided the space up with bookshelves to make a series of little rooms, and put armchairs about with worn cretonne covers, and reading lamps, and made a play area for children with toys on a rug and a rocking horse. She made friends of her customers; she encouraged them to read. They brought photographs of their grandchildren to show her, and batches of cookies and problems. Sometimes, I must admit, I was jealous of her customers.

She also had festivals in the store.

At Hallowe'en she filled the window with pumpkins and witches' hats and at the New Year, she dressed it up for Scottish Hogmanay with antlers and tartan ribbons. None of that I minded; indeed, I applauded her enterprise. But at Easter, and at Christmas, I cringed. I pleaded with her every year not to give way to cheap sentiment, to superstition, but she took no notice, she went ahead. Year after year, twice a year, I had to endure the spectacle, in this remarkable store that was a shrine to the glory of the English language, of a holy garden at Easter and a crib at Christmas.

My mother made the garden

herself every year, with mosses and spring flowers, and a cave built of stones collected on Sunday walks in the woods. The crib she had bought on her honeymoon in southern France, in Provence. It was made of some kind of pottery clay, easily chipped and crudely painted. She set it up in the children's corner between two candles, in a ruff of ivy, and it caused me, her own and only child, mortification of the acutest kind.

When she died, I felt I had two choices. Either I allowed the bookstore to remain exactly the same, a shrine to her memory, or I made some changes. I decided upon the latter. I am a better businesswoman than my mother, and although I have inherited her love of literature, I am not alarmed by technology as she was, nor opposed to the commercial sense of stocking business and computer books. I cleaned up the store a little. I took away most of the armchairs because too many people had become accustomed to lunching in them and I did not want my stock spoiled by smears of tuna mayonnaise. I changed my mother's sentimental festivals into book-orientated festivals to celebrate a prizewinning novel, a major biography, a breakthrough cookbook. I held business-book seminars at lunchtime and poetry readings at night. I started a gift-wrapping service and opened discount accounts for local schools and companies.

My mother's customers told me the store had lost its heart. I refrained from telling them that it was no longer losing money. My grief for my mother might make me resentful at any implied criticism of my treatment of her memory, but it wasn't going to make me forget my manners. The store was not as full as it had been when my mother was alive – sometimes it had resembled a bridal shower in noise and atmosphere – but I had three times the number of account customers, most of them institutions. I had to hire a boy to help with the packing.

At night, when I had finally closed the store and set the new security alarm, I would go up to the apartment above and drink a single glass of wine. Merlot was my choice usually; sometimes I drank a Cabernet Sauvignon. When I had drunk my wine, I fixed myself something quick to eat in the microwave, and then I would settle down with a mug of coffee – Costa Rica, medium roast – to my mother's papers. It was an indulgence, a nightly fix as cherished as the glass of Merlot.

It took me almost a year and a half to get through everything my mother left – diaries, letters, photographs, playbills, cuttings, reviews, notes and quotations scribbled on the backs of envelopes.

'I can't tell you everything that's happened to me,' my mother said before she died. 'I've forgotten the half of it. But you will find everything you want to know. It's all there.'

I read everything. I am a methodical person, and I discarded nothing before reading it. I made scrapbooks and collections of letters in labelled boxes. I put pictures into chronological order and slid them into the vinyl pockets of albums. I copied quotations into a commonplace book, and made a history of the founding of the bookstore in a green boxfile. I hoped it would be a therapy for me, but it was the reverse. Every night I longed to find something that would reconcile me to my mother's passing, and every night she rose before me, more vivid than ever, and I missed her wretchedly. I even felt – and I am aware this is unjust – that she, with her English heritage and English assumptions, had left me stranded here alone in a country which was my birthplace but to which, because of her, I could never quite belong.

I also felt estranged by her Catholic upbringing. There were several rosaries in her drawers, and a couple of prayer books, and above her bed had always hung a reproduction of a

Della Robbia Madonna and Child, a blue-and-white porcelain plaque. I left all these things where I found them, but I would have preferred them out of the way. Just as I would have preferred my mother – so intelligent, so warm and witty, who scarcely in my lifetime even entered a church – not to have clung so blindly to these leftover trappings of a child's past. It sometimes seemed to me like a dreadful falseness in a person otherwise so transparently honest. But we didn't talk about it. It was the only thing we didn't talk about. She said that there was no point, because she could see that my mind was made up.

Early last December, we had
some terrible rains. It wasn't cold,
but it was wild and wet and windy
and the weather kept customers
away. A businessman, whom I sup-
plied with computer books, said that
I should consider re-locating to the
new shopping mall outside our
town where there was all-weather
parking. I told him I would then
suffer from the proximity of a big
chain bookstore, offering immense
discounts, and he gave me a con-
sidering look and I could see he
knew about the immense discounts
already, and was turning his loyalty
to me over in his mind.

When he had gone, I closed the
store early and went upstairs to my

apartment. It was not time yet for my ritual glass of Merlot, so instead I obeyed my mother's lifelong habit and made a pot of loose-leaf Lapsang Souchong tea. I took this with me into my living room and put on the lamps and pulled the drapes against the wet black evening. Only one drawer of my mother's papers remained to me, and I was dreading its being sorted.

It lay on the rug in front of the electric fire my mother had insisted upon as reminding her of England. I put my tea down on the floor and then I knelt down and lifted out a heap of assorted envelopes in which mail had come over the years and which my mother thriftily hoarded.

One of them was large and bulky. It had come from Hatchards, the English bookstore in Piccadilly, London, and had probably contained a catalogue. Now it had a white gummed label stuck across it, not quite straight, on which my mother had written in her bold hand 'About my father'.

I untucked the flap of the envelope and held it open over my hearthrug. A shower of papers fell out, newspaper cuttings mostly, and a memo badly typed on sheets of thin white paper held together with a rusting clip. I unfolded some of the cuttings. They were from English newspapers, some provincial, some national, and there were disturbing headlines: 'Theatre Manager's Theft'; 'Manager Defrauds Theatre'; 'Hand in the Box Office Till'. I picked up the memo. I could see at once from the way it was typed that it had been typed by my mother. It had no heading, only a date – November 1956. In 1956 I was twelve, and my mother's bookstore was only two years old. By 1956 my English grandfather had been a widower for sixteen years.

I quickly saw that the memo had not merely been typed by my mother, but written by her, too. She described my grandfather, so wedded to his theatre that he was there seven days a week, and six nights a week, too, dressed in a black evening suit with a stiff-fronted white shirt and a black bow tie, welcoming theatregoers into the foyer. She described herself, too, going to the theatre as a child with her father and standing on the empty stage listening to the seats tipping up in the empty auditorium as the temperature changed, as if a ghostly audience waited in perpetuity for the show to begin.

She said my grandfather did everything in that theatre. It belonged to the Town Council, who furnished a board of trustees like characters from an Arnold Bennett novel, bluff, uncompromising, respectable northern citizens. Once a month, my grandfather reported to the board of trustees and wrestled with their lack of imagination, their deep-seated philistinism. In the early spring of 1956, after thirty-five years of unremitting labour for the theatre, my grandfather asked for a few months' leave of absence. He gave the trustees to understand that he would be visiting his daughter and granddaughter in America. The trustees, much startled, eventually agreed, as long as he took it upon himself to find a temporary manager.

My grandfather did find a manager, but he did not come to America. Instead, he went in search of a place that my mother said had been the dream passion of his life; he went, alone, to look for the seat of King Arthur, for the site of Camelot.

It took him three months. He went from Caerleon upon Usk to Winchester, and from thence to Cadbury Camp near Queen Camel in Somerset and to Tintagel in the Camel county of Cornwall. He hired a good automobile and stayed in good hotels. He kept a comprehensive and scholarly journal which he bequeathed at his death to a northern university to assist those studying the legends of King Arthur and the works of the poet Tennyson. And while he was away the temporary manager discovered – with no difficulty since my grandfather had scarcely troubled to conceal it – that the funds used to pay for this comfortable and chimerical journey had been removed from the straitened coffers of the theatre.

My grandfather was summoned before the trustees. He was perfectly open. He had no defence beyond this longing that had built up to a craving to find the place that had so seized upon his mind. He was perfectly happy to repay the funds by working for no more than a pittance until the debt was cleared. He then stood and looked at those solid, practical northern faces, and waited for certain dismissal and probable arrest.

'And did you,' one trustee asked, 'find Camelot?'

My grandfather admitted that he had failed.

'Then we may assume that you no longer believe in the possibility of its existence?'

My grandfather was deeply shocked. 'Oh no,' he said, in gentle reproof, 'I believe as I ever did.'

The trustees let him keep his job. 'It was the only moment,' my mother wrote, 'in all his dealings with them, when he felt that their minds were in tune with his.'

I put the memo down and merely sat there on my living-room floor. My tea had grown quite cold. I sat there for perhaps half an hour and then I rose, rather stiffly, and went into the little room my mother had always called the box room, in her English way, where we kept the lumber of our lives. I hunted about among the bundles and bales until I found the cardboard box containing the little crib figures from Provence, and I carried it down to the darkened and empty store.

There was just enough light coming in from the street to illumine what I wanted to do. I cleared a space in the window in the display of Christmas cookery books I had arranged among ivy trails and decorative pyramids of clementines and walnuts, and in it I set out the Virgin Mary in her blue robe and Joseph in his brown one and the baby in his bed of stiffly painted straw. I added the shepherds to one side and the clumsy ox and ass to the other, and positioned the three Magi at a discreet distance to await the coming of Twelfth Night. Then I fetched from my kitchen one of the slow-burning nightlights my mother had liked by her bed during the last weeks of her life, and lit it, and put it below the figures in a small green saucer. It threw a pool of faint light over the central figures and cast their shadows up against the books behind them. I stood and looked at the scene for a few moments, and then I went back upstairs to pour myself a glass of wine. I am not, as I have said, a religious woman and I never will be. But I knew then – and will now know for ever – the curious power of possibility.

A NOTE ON THE AUTHOR

Joanna Trollope is the author of many
novels and a work of non-fiction,
Britannia's Daughters. Her most recent
novel is *Next of Kin*. She lives in
Gloucestershire.

ALSO AVAILABLE AS BLOOMSBURY QUIDS

Margaret Atwood	*The Labrador Fiasco*
T. Coraghessan Boyle	*She Wasn't Soft*
Nadine Gordimer	*Harald, Claudia, and their Son Duncan*
David Guterson	*The Drowned Son*
Jay McInerney	*The Queen and I*
Candia McWilliam	*Change of Use*
Will Self	*A Story for Europe*
Patrick Süskind	*Maître Mussard's Bequest*
Tobias Wolff	*Two Boys and a Girl*

AVAILABLE AS BLOOMSBURY CLASSICS

Surfacing, Margaret Atwood
Wilderness Tips, Margaret Atwood
The Snow Queen and Other Fairy Stories,
   Hans Christian Andersen
At The Jerusalem, Paul Bailey
Old Soldiers, Paul Bailey
Flaubert's Parrot, Julian Barnes
Ten, A Bloomsbury Tenth Anniversary Anthology
The Piano, Jane Campion and Kate Pullinger
The Passion of New Eve, Angela Carter
Emperor of the Air, Ethan Canin
Alice's Adventures in Wonderland, Lewis Carroll
A Christmas Carol, Charles Dickens
Poor Cow, Nell Dunn
The Lover, Marguerite Duras
The Birds of the Air, Alice Thomas Ellis
The Virgin Suicides, Jeffrey Eugenides
Utopia and Other Places, Richard Eyre
The Great Gatsby, F. Scott Fitzgerald
Bad Girls, Mary Flanagan
The Lagoon and Other Stories, Janet Frame
Mona Minim, Janet Frame
Owls Do Cry, Janet Frame
Across the Bridge, Mavis Gallant
Green Water, Green Sky, Mavis Gallant
Something Out There, Nadine Gordimer
Christmas Stories, Selected by Giles Gordon
Ghost Stories, Selected by Giles Gordon
Carol, Patricia Highsmith
The 158-Pound Marriage, John Irving
Setting Free the Bears, John Irving
Trying to Save Piggy Sneed, John Irving

Jimmy and the Desperate Woman, D. H. Lawrence
Einstein's Dreams, Alan Lightman
Bright Lights, Big City, Jay McInerney
Debatable Land, Candia McWilliam
Bliss and Other Stories, Katherine Mansfield
The Garden Party and Other Stories, Katherine Mansfield
So Far from God, Patrick Marnham
Lies of Silence, Brian Moore
The Lonely Passion of Judith Hearne, Brian Moore
The Pumpkin Eater, Penelope Mortimer
Lives of Girls and Women, Alice Munro
The Country Girls, Edna O'Brien
Coming Through Slaughter, Michael Ondaatje
The English Patient, Michael Ondaatje
In the Skin of a Lion, Michael Ondaatje
Running in the Family, Michael Ondaatje
Let Them Call it Jazz, Jean Rhys
Wide Sargasso Sea, Jean Rhys
Keepers of the House, Lisa St Aubin de Téran
The Quantity Theory of Insanity, Will Self
The Pigeon, Patrick Süskind
The Heather Blazing, Colm Tóibín
Cocktails at Doney's and Other Stories, William Trevor
The Choir, Joanna Trollope
Angel, All Innocence, Fay Weldon
Oranges are not the only fruit, Jeanette Winterson
The Passion, Jeanette Winterson
Sexing the Cherry, Jeanette Winterson
In Pharaoh's Army, Tobias Wolff
This Boy's Life, Tobias Wolff
Orlando, Virginia Woolf
A Room of One's Own, Virginia Woolf